SCHOLASTIC

Maths Practice for

Year 6

Ages 10-11

This book belongs to:

Maths Year 6, Book 1

Book End, Range Road, Witney, Oxfordshire, OX29 0YD
Registered office: Westfield Road, Southam, Warwickshire CV47 0RA
www.scholastic.co.uk

© 2015, Scholastic Ltd

3 4 5 6 7 8 9   6 7 8 9 0 1 2 3 4 5

British Library Cataloguing-in-Publication Data
A catalogue record for this book is available from the British Library.

ISBN 978-1407-14215-9
Printed in Malaysia

Due to the nature of the web we cannot guarantee the content or links of any
site mentioned. We strongly recommend that teachers check websites before
using them in the classroom.

Editorial
Rachel Morgan, Robin Hunt, Kate Baxter, John Davis, Mark Walker

Design
Scholastic Design Team: Neil Salt, Nicolle Thomas
and Oxford Designers & Illustrators Ltd

Cover Design
Neil Salt

Illustration
Tomek.gr

Contents

Why buy this book?

This series has been designed to support the introduction of the new National Curriculum in schools in England. The new curriculum is more challenging in mathematics and includes the requirement for children's understanding to be secure before moving on. These practice books will help your child revise and practise all of the skills they will learn at school, and including some topics they might not have encountered previously.

How to use this book

- The content is divided into National Curriculum topics (for example, Addition and subtraction, Fractions and so on). Find out what your child is doing in school and dip into the relevant practice activities as required.

- Share the activities and support your child if necessary using the helpful quick tips at the top of most pages.

- Keep the working time short and come back to an activity if your child finds it too difficult. Ask your child to note any areas of difficulty at the back of the book. Don't worry if your child does not 'get' a concept first time, as children learn at different rates and content is likely to be covered throughout the school year.

- Check your child's answers using the answers section at the back of the book.

- Give lots of encouragement and tick off the progress chart as your child completes each chapter.

How to use the book

This tells you which topic you're working on.

This is the title of the activity.

These boxes will help you with the activity.

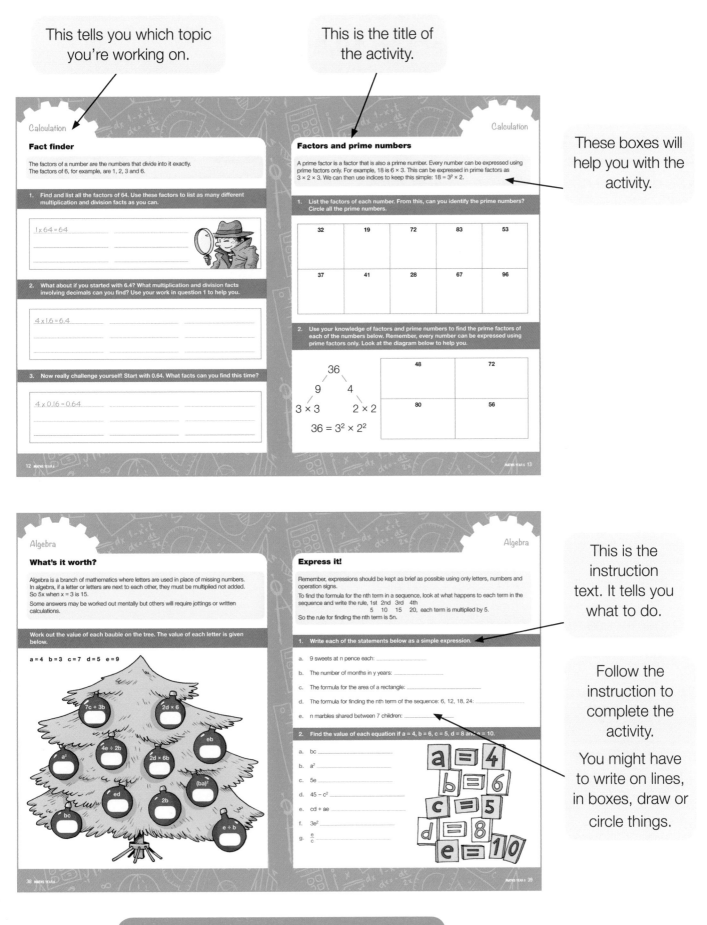

This is the instruction text. It tells you what to do.

Follow the instruction to complete the activity.

You might have to write on lines, in boxes, draw or circle things.

If you need help, ask an adult!

Read and write numbers to 10,000,000

Practise and make sure that you have a good understanding and use of six-digit numbers before going on to millions up to ten million. Continue to use abacus frameworks if you have difficulty knowing where to position zeros as place holders.

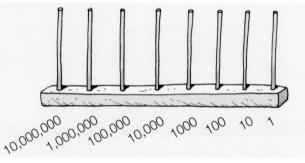

10,000,000   1,000,000   100,000   10,000   1000   100   10   1

1. Write these amounts in figures.

a. six hundred and one _____

b. four thousand and nine _____

c. twenty thousand, six hundred and three _____

d. one million, six hundred and twenty thousand, four hundred and ninety-one _____

e. four hundred and seven thousand, one hundred and seven _____

f. twenty-six thousand, three hundred _____

g. three hundred thousand _____

h. four thousand, nine hundred _____

i. two million, four hundred and seven thousand, five hundred and eighty-three _____

j. fifty-three thousand, seven hundred and twenty-four _____

k. eighty thousand and five _____

l. six hundred and ten _____

m. eighty thousand, five hundred _____

n. twenty thousand, six hundred and thirty _____

o. four thousand and ninety _____

2. Write these amounts in words.

a. 3020 _____

b. 8200 _____

c. 27,506 _____

d. 708,090 _____

e. 4,780,909 _____

_____

3. How many:

a. thousands in 1,275,320? _____

b. hundreds in 4,008,957? _____

c. tens in 2,697,000? _____

4. Write the decimal fraction equivalent to these amounts.

a. three tenths _____

b. 5 hundredths _____

c. 12 thousandths _____

d. 8 tenths _____

e. 200 thousandths _____

f. $\frac{23}{100}$ _____

g. $\frac{4}{20}$ _____

h. forty hundredths _____

Rounding whole numbers

Rounding numbers helps to provide us with approximate answers. This is useful when we want to check if a calculation is likely to be correct. For example, rounding 39 × 41 to 40 × 40 = 1600 gives us a result that is close to the correct answer (1599).

1. Round these amounts to the nearest:

a. £100	b. 1000km	c. 10,000 miles
£4251	$500\frac{1}{2}$km	52,836 miles
_____	_____	_____
£36,749	3499km	460,001 miles
_____	_____	_____
£843,001	8620.3km	790,999 miles
_____	_____	_____
£949.99	483,995km	854,030 miles
_____	_____	_____

2. Round these lengths to the nearest cm.

a. 851mm _____   b. 4439mm _____

c. 7904mm _____

3. Round these amounts to the nearest 1000kg.

a. 599.5kg _____   b. 44,499kg _____

c. 102,453kg _____

4. Write some examples of amounts you would round to the nearest 10, 100, 1000 and 10,000, e.g. the crowd at a Grand Prix would be rounded to the nearest 1000.

a. 10 _____   b. 100 _____

c. 1000 _____   d. 10,000 _____

Positive and negative

When working with positive and negative numbers you may find it easier to put your pencil point on the number line and count the steps physically. Remember that moving in a positive direction goes to the right, and moving in a negative direction to the left.

1. Use the number line to help you solve these problems.

-10 -9 -8 -7 -6 -5 -4 -3 -2 -1 0 1 2 3 4 5 6 7 8 9 10

a. Start at −5 and jump three spaces in a positive direction. Where do you land? _____

b. Start at 4 and jump eight spaces in a negative direction. Where do you land? _____

c. Start at 9 and jump fifteen spaces in a negative direction. Where do you land? _____

d. Moving in a positive direction, give the next three numbers in this sequence.

−9   −6   −3   ☐   ☐   ☐

e. Moving in a negative direction, give the next three numbers in this sequence.

10   6   2   ☐   ☐   ☐

f. Put these numbers in order of size, starting with the largest.

−3   −1   4   0   6   2   _____

g. Put these numbers in order of size, starting with the smallest.

0   5   −4   −2   7   −8   _____

h. Fill in the gaps to complete this number pattern.

☐   −5   −2   ☐   ☐   7

Number problems with big numbers

1000 thousand is called a million. It has six zeros: 1,000,000.
Half a million is half of 1000 thousand: 500,000. A quarter of a million is half of this: 250,000, and three quarters of a million is a half and a quarter added together:
500,000 + 250,000 = 750,000.

1. Rewrite in figures the amounts in these newspaper headlines.

a. Half a million working days lost _____

b. £$2\frac{1}{2}$ million bingo win _____

c. £$5\frac{1}{4}$ million spending cuts _____

d. Massive cash robbery of £$6\frac{1}{2}$ million _____

e. Britain has 445 million kilometres of roads _____

2. Write in figures the number that is half a million less than the following.

a. 6 million _____   b. 800,000 _____

c. $7\frac{3}{4}$ million _____

3. Write in figures the number that is 200,000 more than the following.

a. 1 million _____   b. 6,500,000 _____

c. $4\frac{1}{4}$ million _____

4. What is the value of each circled digit?

a. 1,2⑥4,319 _____   b. ④,375,610 _____

c. 840,①23 _____   d. 1,②34,567 _____

e. 534,01⑦ _____   f. ①0,500,000 _____

Negative number problems

Temperatures are measured in degrees, on a thermometer using the Celsius scale (°C).
Numbers above zero are positive numbers (above freezing point). Numbers below zero are
negative numbers (below freezing point).

1. **Chilly Billy is in Iceland where the temperature is −14°C.
    Sunshine Sue is in Florida where the temperature is 33°C.**

    What is the difference between the two temperatures? _____

2. **The following week, the temperature in Iceland drops by 7°C and the
    temperature in Florida rises by 6°C.**

    What is the new temperature in Iceland? _____

    What is the new temperature in Florida? _____

    What is difference between the two temperatures? _____

3. **The coldest temperature ever recorded in Iceland is −39°C. The hottest
    temperature ever recorded in Florida is 43°C.**

    What is the difference, in degrees Celsius, between these record temperatures?

    _____

Fact finder

The factors of a number are the numbers that divide into it exactly.
The factors of 6, for example, are 1, 2, 3 and 6.

1. **Find and list all the factors of 64. Use these factors to list as many different multiplication and division facts as you can.**

$1 \times 64 = 64$

2. **What about if you started with 6.4? What multiplication and division facts involving decimals can you find? Use your work in question 1 to help you.**

$4 \times 1.6 = 6.4$

3. **Now really challenge yourself! Start with 0.64. What facts can you find this time?**

$4 \times 0.16 = 0.64$

Factors and prime numbers

A prime factor is a factor that is also a prime number. Every number can be expressed using prime factors only. For example, 18 is 6 × 3. This can be expressed in prime factors as 3 × 2 × 3. We can then use indices to keep this simple: $18 = 3^2 \times 2$.

1. List the factors of each number. From this, can you identify the prime numbers? Circle all the prime numbers.

32	19	72	83	53
37	41	28	67	96

2. Use your knowledge of factors and prime numbers to find the prime factors of each of the numbers below. Remember, every number can be expressed using prime factors only. Look at the diagram below to help you.

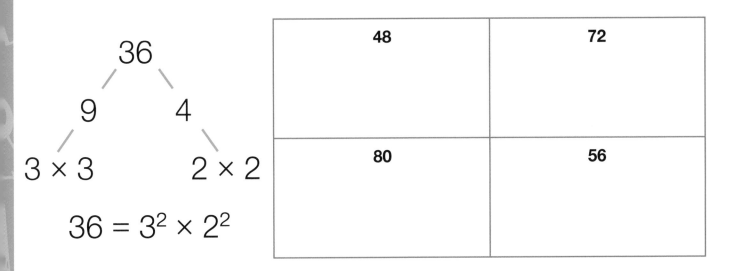

36

9   4

3 × 3   2 × 2

$36 = 3^2 \times 2^2$

48	72
80	56

Long multiplication

```
  2 3 1
1 3 5 2
×    2 7
2 7 0 4 0
  9 4 6 4
3 6 5 0 4
1     1
```

In this example:

Always write the numbers in the correct columns.

Remember to add a 0 before multiplying by 2 because it is two 10s.

Carried figures should be added on to the next stage.

Both lines of working out should be totalled.

1. Use a compact written method of long multiplication to solve the following.

a. 387 × 36

b. 439 × 28

c. 1538 × 47

d. 5125 × 39

e. 5600 × 49

f. 7089 × 81

g. 3002 × 73

h. 9909 × 56

Long multiplication problem

It is important that you use the compact written method for long multiplication. Make sure you include all your working out.

How many slices of bread would you eat in 25 years? 10,000? 20,000? More? Less? Now is you chance to find out!

1. First of all, write an estimate here: _____ slices of bread.

2. What calculation strategies could help you? What will you need to do first? Use the box below to write down some ideas.

3. Now use long multiplication to complete your calculations.

4. I eat _____ slices of bread in 25 years.

5. Do you eat more or less than you

   estimated? _____

Adding order

Numbers can be added in any order and they will still produce the same total. Rearrange the order in your head before you start to add them mentally. It may be helpful to start with the largest number first and then continue going down in order of size.

1. Rearrange and then complete these calculations in your head so that you start with the largest amount. Remember to look for the number bonds.

a. 14 + 40 + 1210 + 56 + 17 = _____

b. 38 + 40 + 27 + 2750 + 33 = _____

c. 60 + 25 + 45 + 56 + 8530 = _____

d. 45 + 6480 + 70 + 42 + 58 = _____

e. 320km + 426km + 1580km = _____

f. 770kg + 4030kg + 659kg = _____

g. £942 + £840 + £9360 = _____

h. 220ml + 6780ml + 50ml = _____

2. Answer these questions. Think about putting the largest number first.

a. What amount results from adding £2.40, £4.60, £1.25 and £1.75?

_____

b. Find the total of six, sixty, six hundred and six thousand and six.

_____

c. Increase four hundred and seventy by five thousand, three hundred and thirty, and then increase the result by one million, three hundred and ten.

_____

School trip division

$$6\overline{)1\ 9^1 2}$$ $3\ 2$

When you do short division, make sure you keep the digits in the correct columns. In this example (192 divided by 6), 6 into 19 goes 3 times with one 10 left over. The 3 is written in the 10s column and the one 10 is carried over to the 1s, joining with the 2 to make 12; when 12 is divided by 6, it goes twice with no remainder.

Here are the ticket prices for the different school trips that have been arranged for the summer term.

1. **If this was the money collected for each trip, work out how many tickets were bought by the pupils.**

a. Theatre £376

Answer: _____ tickets

b. Water World £675

Answer: _____ tickets

c. Safari Park £1164

Answer: _____ tickets

d. Concert £882

Answer: _____ tickets

e. Football match £1170

Answer: _____ tickets

f. Theme Park £1344

Answer: _____ tickets

Calculation

Long division

$$\begin{array}{r} 24 \\ 18\overline{)447} \\ 360 \\ 87 \\ 72 \\ 15 \end{array}$$

18×20

18×4

$\frac{15}{18} = \frac{5}{6}$

Answer: $24\frac{5}{6}$

In long division it is very important to keep the columns correctly positioned with 1s under 1s, 10s under 10s and so on.

First, divide 44 by 18. It goes twice, write 2 above the 10s column. It does not go exactly, so work out 18 × 20 (360) and subtract it from 447 to get 87.

Then divide 87 by 18. It goes four times, write 4 above the 1s column. It does not go exactly, so work out 18 × 4 (72) and subtract it from 87 to get 15.

Write the remainder as a fraction of the divisor, that is, the number you are dividing by (18 in this case). Finally, write the fraction in its lowest term. $\frac{15}{18}$ can be expressed as $\frac{5}{6}$.

1. Use long division to solve the following. If there is a remainder, state this as a fraction.

a. 360 ÷ 15

Answer: _____

b. 476 ÷ 14

Answer: _____

c. 986 ÷ 17

Answer: _____

d. 1625 ÷ 25

Answer: _____

e. 760 ÷ 16

Answer: _____

f. 930 ÷ 24

Answer: _____

g. 852 ÷ 18

Answer: _____

h. 1030 ÷ 15

Answer: _____

Long division target practice

Use your division skills to hit the target.

1. Choose a number from each bag.
   Each number can only be used once.

2. Use long division to make a number
   from the target board.

3. Estimate first, as it will help you to choose the
   correct pair of numbers. The first one has
   been done for you.

Remember: The first two digits to be divided are
the most important to help with estimating as they
will give you the first digit of the target number.

149
102
205   138
32
22
109
112
176   622

9   12   7
11   4   15
8   10   6   18

576   894   2050
4976   1530   704
1232   966   264   981

109 9)981				

Soup factory division

It is important to remember that both multiplication and subtraction are involved in the division process. It may help with a calculation if you work out some of the multiples of the divisor first by adding on. For example, multiples of 18 would be 18, 36, 54, 72, 90, and so on.

Rosa works in a soup factory, in the packaging section.

1. Use long division to calculate how many boxes she will need to pack the following flavours of soup. Show all your workings.

Remember: you may need to round up if there are tins left over.

a. **Tomato:** 1224 tins in boxes of 12

_____ boxes

b. **Chicken:** 1368 tins in boxes of 18

_____ boxes

c. **Oxtail:** 3227 tins in boxes of 15

_____ boxes

d. **Vegetable:** 3000 tins in boxes of 24

_____ boxes

e. **Minestrone:** 6989 tins in boxes of 32

_____ boxes

Round up and down

Some divisions will need to be rounded up or down, depending on the context.

230 people need to travel on 18-seater buses. How many buses are needed? This answer will be rounded up as you will need to seat all the people. 230 ÷ 18 = 12, remainder 14. So 13 buses are needed.

230 pens are packed 18 to each box. How many complete boxes are there? This answer will be rounded down as the question asks for the number of *complete* boxes: 12 boxes.

1. **Calculate the answer to each question. There will be a remainder. Decide whether you need to round the answer up or down to answer the question.**

a. A garden centre plants seedlings in trays of 35. How many complete trays can be filled with 456 seedlings?

_____ trays

b. Crayons are packed in boxes of 15. How many full boxes can be made from a pile of 456 crayons?

_____ boxes

c. Thirty-eight people can sit in a row of seats at the hockey stadium. How many rows are needed to seat 1200 spectators?

_____ rows

d. A jug holds 750ml of liquid. How many jugs will be needed to hold 8 litres of orange juice?

_____ jugs

e. A bus company has 28-seater buses. If 520 people want to go on a trip to the zoo, how many buses are needed to take them?

_____ buses

Postal addition problem

Josh and Raj have some packages to post to different countries. They have a sheet of 5p stamps, a sheet of 16p stamps and a sheet of 23p stamps.

- Josh says: "I don't know how much the postage is for each of these packages but it is somewhere between 30p and 40p."
- Raj says: "That's OK, as there is only one amount over 30p that we can't make with these stamps."

1. Is Raj right? Show, with workings, which amounts between 30p and 40p you can make using 5p, 16p, and 23p stamps. It may help to try out some amounts on scrap paper first before starting to fill in the boxes on the page.

Amount	5p	16p	23p	Workings
30p				
31p				
32p				
33p				
34p				
35p				
36p				
37p				
38p				
39p				
40p				

Missing information problems

1. **There is an important piece of information missing from each of these word problems. Decide what information you need before the problems can be solved.**

2. **When you have decided what piece of information is missing, make up numbers for this part of the question and solve the problem. Show all your calculations. Estimate each answer first, and then find a way of checking it afterwards.**

a. Alan, Sunil, Martha and Emma collect football cards. If Alan has 57 cards, Sunil 29 cards and Martha 63 cards, how many cards do the four children have altogether?

b. Maths lessons take place each day in school. How long do maths lessons last in total during a normal school week?

c. A farmer divides 345 sheep into equal numbers to put them into pens. How many sheep are there in each pen?

d. Stacey is training for a swimming race. She swims 500 metres every weekday, but more at weekends. How far does she swim in a complete week?

Estimating costs

1. **Estimate the cost of these tickets. You can round the prices to the nearest £10, £50 or £100.**

   a. Four tickets to Greece _____

   b. Three tickets to USA _____

   c. Five tickets to Spain _____

   d. Two tickets to France and three tickets to Spain _____

2. **Now work out the exact cost. How close were your estimates?**

   a.

   b.

   c.

   d.

Common factors and simplifying fractions

A common factor is a factor that is common to two or more numbers.

To simplify a fraction, or reduce it to its lowest terms, you need to divide the numerator and denominator by a common factor.

For $\frac{12}{15}$: 3 is a common factor of both 12 and 15, as 3 into 12 will go 4 times and 3 into 15 will go 5 times. So $\frac{12}{15}$ can be simplified to $\frac{4}{5}$.

The highest common factor (HCF) is the largest factor that is common to a set of any given numbers. For 16 and 24, the common factors are 2, 4 and 8, so the HCF is 8.

1. Write all the common factors of each pair of numbers.

a. 6, 10: _____

b. 12, 20: _____

c. 8, 10: _____

d. 12, 36: _____

e. 8, 12: _____

f. 45, 30: _____

g. 16, 18: _____

h. 50, 40: _____

2. Write down the highest common factor of each pair of numbers.

a. 9, 12: _____

b. 20, 50: _____

c. 15, 20: _____

d. 28, 42: _____

e. 20, 16: _____

f. 32, 48: _____

g. 30, 24: _____

h. 60, 40: _____

3. **Simplify the following fractions to their lowest terms. This will mean dividing the numerator and denominator by the HCF.**

a. $\frac{6}{8}$ = _____

b. $\frac{5}{10}$ = _____

c. $\frac{4}{12}$ = _____

d. $\frac{15}{25}$ = _____

e. $\frac{20}{30}$ = _____

f. $\frac{60}{100}$ = _____

g. $\frac{9}{27}$ = _____

h. $\frac{20}{24}$ = _____

i. $\frac{14}{42}$ = _____

j. $\frac{36}{40}$ = _____

k. $\frac{16}{36}$ = _____

l. $\frac{95}{100}$ = _____

4. **Simplify the following improper fractions. Change them to whole or mixed numbers first.**

a. $\frac{18}{3}$ = _____

b. $\frac{10}{9}$ = _____

c. $\frac{12}{10}$ = _____

d. $\frac{21}{5}$ = _____

e. $\frac{38}{4}$ = _____

f. $\frac{26}{10}$ = _____

g. $\frac{39}{9}$ = _____

h. $\frac{51}{12}$ = _____

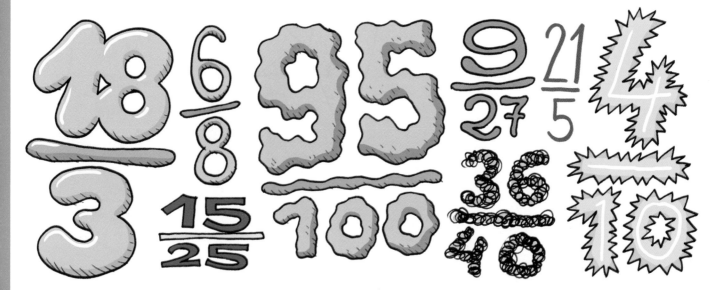

Add and subtract fractions

It is easy to add or subtract fractions if they have the same denominator,

For example, $\frac{3}{5} + \frac{1}{5} = \frac{4}{5}$ and $\frac{5}{6} - \frac{4}{6} = \frac{1}{6}$.

If they have different denominators then first convert them so they have a common

denominator, for example, $\frac{2}{5} + \frac{3}{10} = \frac{4}{10} + \frac{3}{10} = \frac{7}{10}$ and $\frac{5}{6} - \frac{1}{4} = \frac{10}{12} - \frac{3}{12} = \frac{7}{12}$.

1.   Work out each fraction problem by finding a common denominator.

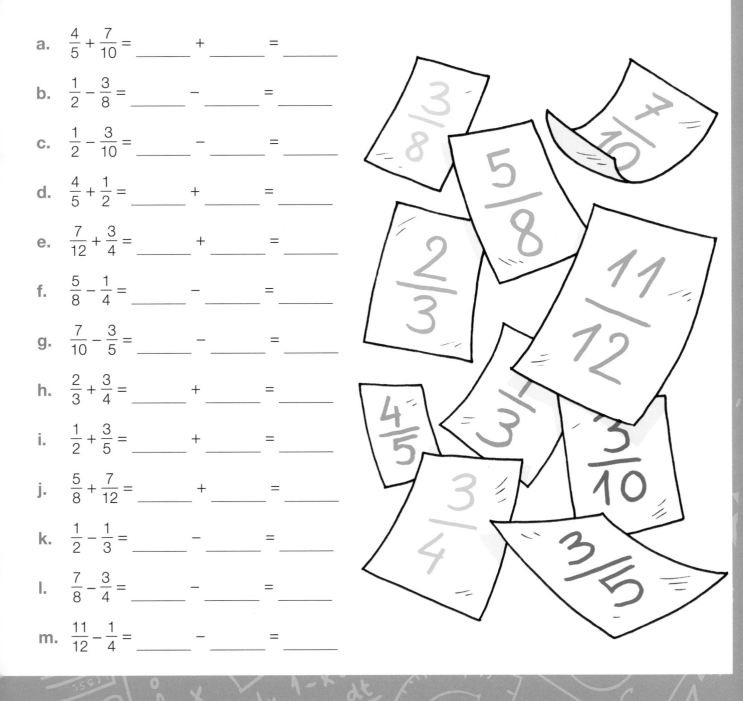

a. $\frac{4}{5} + \frac{7}{10} =$ _____ + _____ = _____

b. $\frac{1}{2} - \frac{3}{8} =$ _____ - _____ = _____

c. $\frac{1}{2} - \frac{3}{10} =$ _____ - _____ = _____

d. $\frac{4}{5} + \frac{1}{2} =$ _____ + _____ = _____

e. $\frac{7}{12} + \frac{3}{4} =$ _____ + _____ = _____

f. $\frac{5}{8} - \frac{1}{4} =$ _____ - _____ = _____

g. $\frac{7}{10} - \frac{3}{5} =$ _____ - _____ = _____

h. $\frac{2}{3} + \frac{3}{4} =$ _____ + _____ = _____

i. $\frac{1}{2} + \frac{3}{5} =$ _____ + _____ = _____

j. $\frac{5}{8} + \frac{7}{12} =$ _____ + _____ = _____

k. $\frac{1}{2} - \frac{1}{3} =$ _____ - _____ = _____

l. $\frac{7}{8} - \frac{3}{4} =$ _____ - _____ = _____

m. $\frac{11}{12} - \frac{1}{4} =$ _____ - _____ = _____

Dividing proper fractions by a whole number

In a fraction, the inverse is made by the numerator changing position with the denominator. The inverse of 2 ($\frac{2}{1}$) is $\frac{1}{2}$ and the inverse of 8 ($\frac{8}{1}$) is $\frac{1}{8}$. Dividing by a number is the same as multiplying by its inverse; so $\frac{2}{3} \div 2$ is the same as $\frac{2}{3} \times \frac{1}{2} = \frac{2}{6}$ or $\frac{1}{3}$.

1.   Divide these fractions by whole numbers.

a. $\frac{2}{3} \div 4 =$ _____

b. $\frac{2}{7} \div 2 =$ _____

c. $\frac{5}{6} \div 10 =$ _____

d. $\frac{4}{5} \div 8 =$ _____

e. $\frac{2}{7} \div 8 =$ _____

f. $\frac{5}{8} \div 10 =$ _____

g. $\frac{5}{9} \div 9 =$ _____

h. $\frac{12}{16} \div 6 =$ _____

i. $\frac{7}{8} \div 14 =$ _____

j. $\frac{5}{6} \div 15 =$ _____

k. $\frac{4}{7} \div 8 =$ _____

l. $\frac{11}{12} \div 4 =$ _____

Multiply pairs of fractions

When multiplying fractions, if no whole numbers are involved, you first multiply the numerators and then multiply the denominators. Look for ways to cancel down so that the answer is always written in its simplest form such as: $\frac{2}{5} \times \frac{3}{8} = \frac{6}{40} = \frac{3}{20}$.

Before multiplying whole or mixed numbers, change them into improper fractions.

So $5 \times \frac{3}{4} = \frac{5}{1} \times \frac{3}{4} = \frac{15}{4} = 3\frac{3}{4}$

$4\frac{2}{3} \times 1\frac{2}{7} = \frac{14}{3} \times \frac{9}{7} = \frac{126}{21} = 6$.

---

1.   Multiply the following pairs of fractions.

a. $\frac{2}{5} \times \frac{1}{2} =$ _____

b. $\frac{3}{4} \times \frac{1}{12} =$ _____

c. $\frac{3}{4} \times \frac{2}{9} =$ _____

d. $\frac{5}{16} \times \frac{4}{5} =$ _____

e. $\frac{4}{9} \times \frac{3}{8} =$ _____

f. $\frac{5}{12} \times \frac{4}{5} =$ _____

g. $\frac{1}{3} \times \frac{9}{10} =$ _____

h. $\frac{2}{5} \times \frac{3}{4} =$ _____

i. $1\frac{1}{4} \times \frac{2}{5} =$ _____

j. $\frac{3}{5} \times 2\frac{1}{2} =$ _____

k. $\frac{4}{7} \times 1\frac{3}{4} =$ _____

l. $2\frac{3}{4} \times \frac{7}{11} =$ _____

m. $1\frac{7}{8} \times 1\frac{3}{5} =$ _____

n. $2\frac{2}{3} \times 1\frac{1}{2} =$ _____

o. $1\frac{7}{8} \times 2\frac{2}{5} =$ _____

p. $2\frac{2}{3} \times 2\frac{1}{4} =$ _____

q. $1\frac{3}{4} \times 1\frac{3}{7} =$ _____

r. $2\frac{1}{4} \times 1\frac{1}{6} =$ _____

s. $1\frac{4}{5} \times 1\frac{1}{4} =$ _____

t. $3\frac{1}{2} \times 1\frac{1}{5} =$ _____

Percentage maker

Remember that 25% = $\frac{1}{4}$, 75% = $\frac{3}{4}$ and 60% = $\frac{6}{10}$. Remember that 15% can be found by finding 10% then halving it to give 5% and adding the two results together. Also, 60% will be six times greater than 10%.

Feed the numbers through the percentage machines to complete each chart. The first one has been partly filled in.

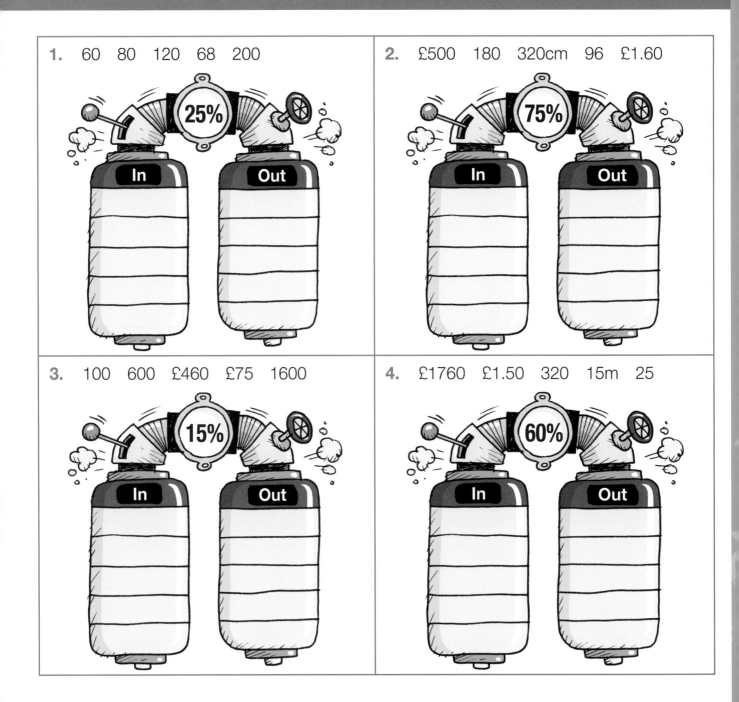

1. 60 80 120 68 200   25% In Out

2. £500 180 320cm 96 £1.60   75% In Out

3. 100 600 £460 £75 1600   15% In Out

4. £1760 £1.50 320 15m 25   60% In Out

Place value in decimals

1. Give the place value of the circled digits in each of the following numbers. Look carefully at the position of the decimal point.

a. 1(5).27 ☐ **b.** 9.(3)6 ☐ **c.** 14.7(5)2 ☐ **d.** 24.0(3) ☐

e. 6.42(9) ☐ **f.** (3)0.054 ☐ **g.** 4(7).002 ☐ **h.** 56.(7)51 ☐

2. What are the values of the letters X, Y and Z?

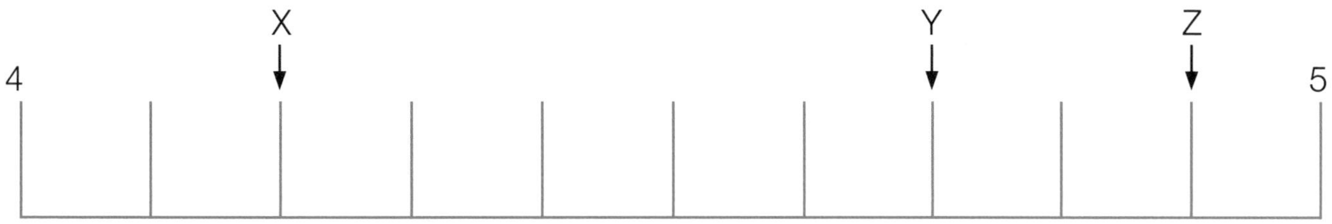

X _____ Y _____ Z _____

3. Draw arrows to show these numbers on the number line.

a. 15.05 **b.** 15.28 **c.** 15.35 **d.** 15.49

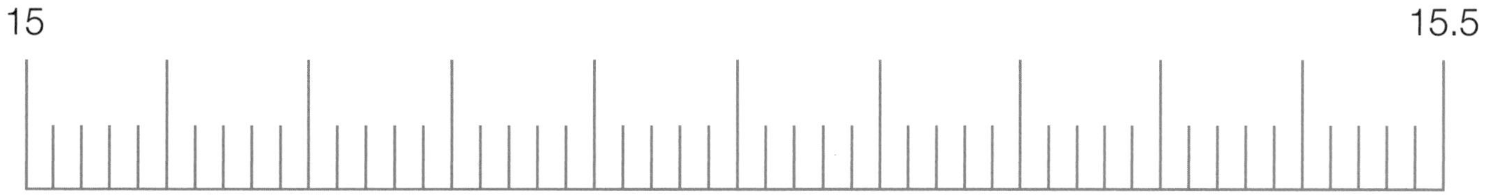

15   15.5

4. Draw arrows to show the approximate positions where these decimal numbers go on the scale. Be as accurate as you can.

a. 0.23 **b.** 1.72 **c.** 0.54 **d.** 1.09 **e.** 1.98

0   1   2

Ratio and proportion

Baking time

To scale ingredients up or down in correct proportions, find out how much is needed for one person and then multiply up or down. So 150g of butter for two people would be 75g of butter for one person, and 75g × 3 = 225g of butter for three people.

1. **These are the ingredients needed for making currant cakes for two people.**

a. How much of each ingredient would you need to make currant cakes for three people?

_____

_____

Currant cakes for two people
2 eggs
120g butter
220g flour
120g currants
60g sugar
60ml milk

b. How much of each ingredient would you need to make currant cakes for five people?

_____

_____

2. **Answer the following questions for the cake recipe for five people.**

a. I have only three eggs. How many more will I need? _____

b. I have 325g of butter. How much will I have left? _____

c. I have 300g of flour. How much more do I need? _____

d. I have 180g of currants. How much more do I need? _____

e. I have a quarter of a litre of milk. How much will I have left? _____

School travel plan

One way of expressing an amount as a percentage of another amount is to first write it as a fraction, and then multiply by 100. So if 105 children out of 250 walk to school this can be written as $\frac{105}{250}$. Simplify the fraction to $\frac{21}{50}$ and then multiply by 100:

$$\frac{21}{50} \times \frac{100}{1} = \frac{2100}{50} = \frac{210}{5} = 42\%$$

There are 280 children in Central School. They have been conducting a survey for their travel plan to find out how children come to school. The table shows what they found out.

Walk to school	112
Come by car	98
By bike	70

1.   What percentage of the children walk?

_____

2.   What percentage come by car?

_____

3.   What percentage cycle?

_____

4.   If 25% more children start walking to school by the end of the year, how many will now be walking?

_____

What's it worth?

Algebra is a branch of mathematics where letters are used in place of missing numbers. In algebra, if a letter or letters are next to each other, they must be multiplied not added. So 5x when x = 3 is 15.

Some answers may be worked out mentally but others will require jottings or written calculations.

Work out the value of each bauble on the tree. The value of each letter is given below.

a = 4   b = 3   c = 7   d = 5   e = 9

7c + 3b

2d × 6

eb

4e ÷ 2b

a^2

2d × 6b

(ba)^2

ed

2b

bc

e ÷ b

Express it!

Remember, expressions should be kept as brief as possible using only letters, numbers and operation signs.

To find the formula for the nth term in a sequence, look at what happens to each term in the sequence and write the rule, 1st 2nd 3rd 4th
 5   10   15   20, each term is multiplied by 5.
So the rule for finding the nth term is 5n.

---

1. **Write each of the statements below as a simple expression.**

a. 9 sweets at n pence each: _____

b. The number of months in y years: _____

c. The formula for the area of a rectangle: _____

d. The formula for finding the nth term of the sequence: 6, 12, 18, 24: _____

e. n marbles shared between 7 children: _____

---

2. **Find the value of each equation if a = 4, b = 6, c = 5, d = 8 and e = 10.**

a. bc _____

b. a^2 _____

c. 5e _____

d. $45 - c^2$ _____

e. cd + ae _____

f. $3e^2$ _____

g. $\dfrac{e}{c}$ _____

Algy and Brian

Substitute the letters for numbers as you work through the problem. Notice that the formula remains the same throughout even when the values of either a or b are changed.

Algy and Brian each represent a different number.

- Algy = a and Brian = b.
- Algy is the number 26.
- $2a = 2b + a$

1. How much is Brian worth?

   _____

2. What is the value of b if a =

   a. 34? _____

   b. 102? _____

3. What is the value of a if b =

   a. 23? [ ]

   b. 54? [ ]

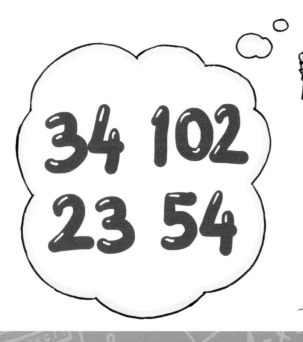

What's next?

Sequences do not always increase by the same interval each time. For example, the sequence +2, +4, +6 would give a pattern of 5, 7, 11, 17 and so on.

Some sequences may have two operations in each step, such as ×2, −1 as in the pattern 10, 20, 21, 42, 43 and so on.

1. **Look carefully at each sequence. For each one, write down the next three numbers or letters in the sequence and explain the rule.**

a. 17   22   28   35   ☐ ☐ ☐   The rule is _____

b. 98   50   26   ☐ ☐ ☐   The rule is _____

c. 25   36   49   ☐ ☐ ☐   The rule is _____

d. $\frac{1}{4}$ $\frac{2}{8}$ $\frac{4}{16}$ ☐ ☐ ☐   The rule is _____

e. A   D   H   ☐ ☐ ☐   The rule is _____

f. 2   7   22   67   ☐ ☐ ☐   The rule is _____

2. **Now write three sequences of your own and explain the rule for each.**

a. ☐ ☐ ☐ ☐ ☐ ☐

The rule is _____

b. ☐ ☐ ☐ ☐ ☐ ☐

The rule is _____

c. ☐ ☐ ☐ ☐ ☐ ☐

The rule is _____

Algebra

In sequence

You may find it useful to explain the rules of a number sequence to someone verbally before writing it down.

1. Give the next four numbers in these sequences. Write the pattern used at the end.

a. 0   5   9   15   18   _____

b. 0   2   8   10   16   _____

c. 3   5.5   8   10.5   13   _____

2. Write in the missing numbers in each of these sequences. Explain the rule that has been used to make the sequence.

a. $\dfrac{23}{8}$ _____ $\dfrac{27}{8}$ _____ $\dfrac{33}{8}$ _____ $\dfrac{41}{8}$

Rule: _____

b. 0.15   0.8   _____   2.1   _____   _____   4.05   _____

Rule: _____

3. This pattern continues in the same way. Answer the questions.

a. Which shape appears in the 28th position? _____

b. How many triangles will there be until you reach the number 40? _____

c. Explain how you found your answers. _____

_____

Algebra problems

Expressions can be simplified by putting the terms together, for example h + h + h can be written as 3h and 5y + 3 + 4 − 2y can be written as 3y + 7. Expressions are also a shorthand way of writing longer number statements or sentences, for example 'Five less than a mystery number' can be written as x − 5.

1. Simplify the following expressions.

a. f + f + f + f = _____

b. 5 + n + 10 = _____

c. g + 6 + g − 8 = _____

d. 2h + h + 3h − h = _____

e. g + g + g + h + h + h = _____

f. 3x + 2y + 2x − y = _____

2. The mystery number is x. Draw a line to match each description in words with the correct expression.

The mystery number multiplied by six and added to two.	x + 3
Two divided by the mystery number.	50 ÷ x
Three more than the mystery number.	6x + 2
The mystery number added to two then multiplied by six.	x²
The mystery number divided by two.	x ÷ 50
The mystery number divided by fifty.	2 ÷ x
Fifty divided by the mystery number.	x ÷ 2
The mystery number multiplied by itself.	6(x + 2)

Estimating length

Make sensible choices when deciding what type of measuring devices you are going to use for each item you measure.

Remember that 10mm = 1cm and 100cm = 1m.

You are going to carry out some measurement tasks at home. You will need a 30cm ruler, a metre stick (or equivalent strip of paper) and a measuring tape.

1. Choose items suitable for the type of measuring device you are using (for example a book for the ruler, a shelf for the metre stick and the length of a room for the tape measure). Aim to measure two or three items with each device.

2. Before you measure each item, estimate how long you think it will be and write down your estimate. When measuring each item, be accurate to the nearest millimetre. If this proves difficult, round to the nearest half-centimetre.

3. Finally, write down the measurements in at least one other way (for example 7cm 8mm could be written as 78mm, 94cm could be written as 0.94m and 5m 17cm could be written as 517cm).

Item measured	Estimate	Measurement	Second recording

Estimating mass

You are going to carry out some measurement tasks. You will need kitchen scales and various objects to weigh. Make sure you ask permission before using anything.

1. Choose a range of objects that will give quite different weights, and spend some time checking you can read information on the scales before weighing. First estimate the weight of each object.

2. Weigh each object to see how accurate your estimate was.

3. Record your information in the chart below, writing the weights in three different ways. Remember: 1250g = 1.25kg = 1kg 250g.

Object	Estimate	Actual weight		
		g	kg	kg and g

Converting units of measures

The location of decimal points will be very important in the answers. There may be some metric units here that you are less familiar with. Note: 1000kg = 1 tonne and 1 centilitre (cl) = 10ml. So 3250kg = 3.250 tonne and 1750ml = 175cl.

Carry out the following conversions between metric units. You will need to use decimal numbers to give the answers.

1. Change from litres to centilitres.	2. Change from centilitres to litres.
a. 11.5 l _____	a. 175cl _____
b. 12.75 l _____	b. 215cl _____
c. 18.5 l _____	c. 870cl _____
d. 22.5 l _____	d. 1460cl _____

3. Change from kilograms to tonnes.	4. Change from tonnes to kilograms.
a. 1275kg _____	a. $4\frac{1}{2}$ tonnes _____
b. 3470kg _____	b. 5.9 tonnes _____
c. 5500kg _____	c. 12.35 tonnes _____
d. 12578kg _____	d. 10.43 tonnes _____

Converting miles to kilometres and vice versa

Remember, the graph must start from zero as no distance has been travelled at this point. If each point is plotted accurately, the graph will form a straight line because the distances increase by the same amount each time. This is known in maths as constant proportion.

1. Mark these distances on the grid to make a straight line graph converting miles into kilometres and vice versa.

Miles	10	20	30	40	50	60	70	80
Kilometres	16	32	48	64	80	96	112	128

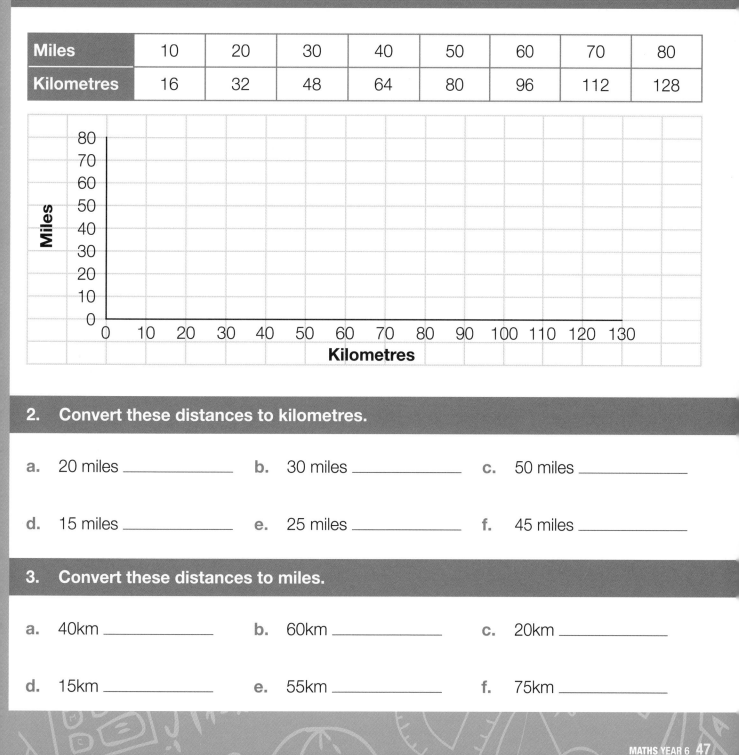

2. Convert these distances to kilometres.

a. 20 miles _____   b. 30 miles _____   c. 50 miles _____

d. 15 miles _____   e. 25 miles _____   f. 45 miles _____

3. Convert these distances to miles.

a. 40km _____   b. 60km _____   c. 20km _____

d. 15km _____   e. 55km _____   f. 75km _____

Same area, different perimeter

Remember, area concerns surface covered, while perimeter is the distance around the outside or edge of a shape. Think of efficient ways to find a perimeter rather than counting squares, such as width + length × 2.

1. Mr Fixit has to build a new patio in the garden of The Crossed Forks restaurant. He has 60 one-metre-square patio slabs. What different rectangular patios can he make with his slabs? Which arrangement gives the biggest perimeter? Record your findings in this chart.

Biggest perimeter: _____

Length	Width	Perimeter

2. The restaurant owners have decided not to have a rectangular patio. Use the squared paper below to find the compound shape (made up of small squares) that will give the greatest perimeter. The patio slabs must fit together side by side – they cannot overlap or join together with just the corners touching. What is the biggest perimeter you can find?

Biggest perimeter: _____

Areas of rooms

Remember that area concerns the surface of a shape while perimeter is the distance around it. You can split compound shapes into convenient rectangles and squares and use the formula for finding the area of a rectangle or square: area = length × width.

The Johnson family is moving house. Sarah Johnson has been looking at details of some of the houses they have been to see because she wants to have the largest bedroom possible.

1. The measurements of the rooms she has seen so far are given below. Work out the floor area of each one to find out which will provide the most space. Write the area in the middle of each shape.

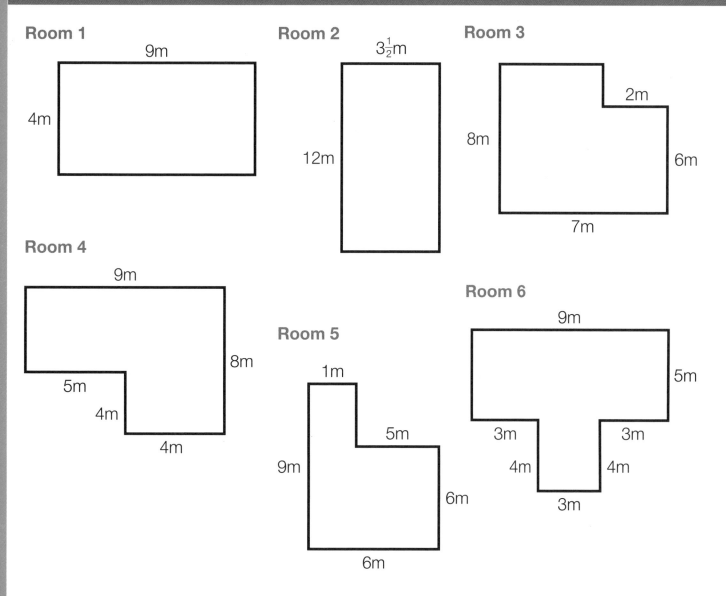

Room 1

9m

4m

Room 2

$3\frac{1}{2}$m

12m

Room 3

2m

8m

6m

7m

Room 4

9m

8m

5m

4m

4m

Room 5

1m

5m

9m

6m

6m

Room 6

9m

5m

3m

3m

4m

4m

3m

Volumes of cubes and cuboids

The volume of 3D shapes is measured in cubic millimetres (mm³), cubic centimetres (cm³) and cubic metres (m³).
The formula for finding the volume of a cube or cuboid is length × width × height.

1. Find the volume of these cubes and cuboids.

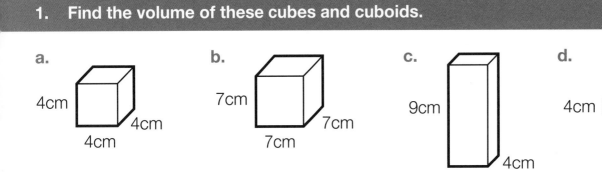

a. _____

b. _____

c. _____

d. _____

e. _____

f. _____

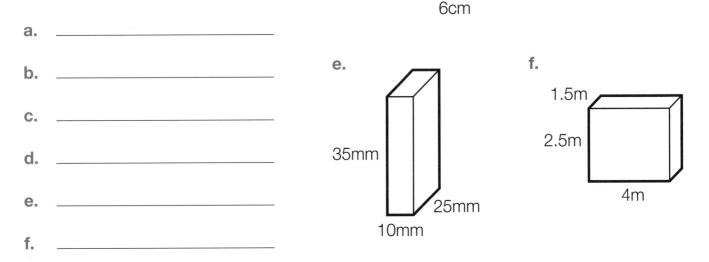

2. This table shows the sizes of some cuboids. Fill in the gap.

Length (cm)	Width (cm)	Height (cm)	Volume (cm³)
4cm	5cm	6cm	
	3cm	4cm	24cm³
4cm		10cm	80cm³
3cm	3cm		117cm³

3. Which of these cuboids have the same volume?

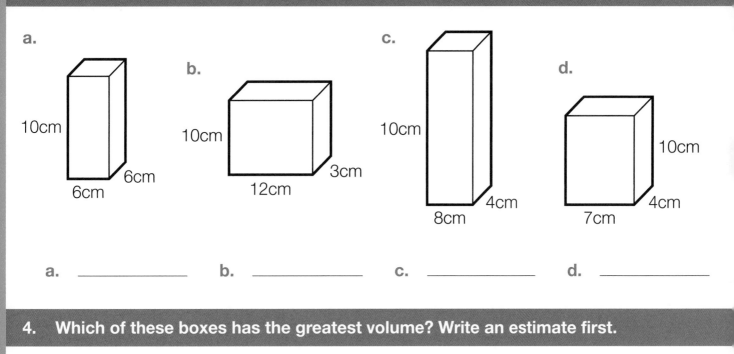

a.

10cm
6cm
6cm

b.

10cm
12cm
3cm

c.

10cm
8cm
4cm

d.

10cm
7cm
4cm

a. _____ b. _____ c. _____ d. _____

4. Which of these boxes has the greatest volume? Write an estimate first.

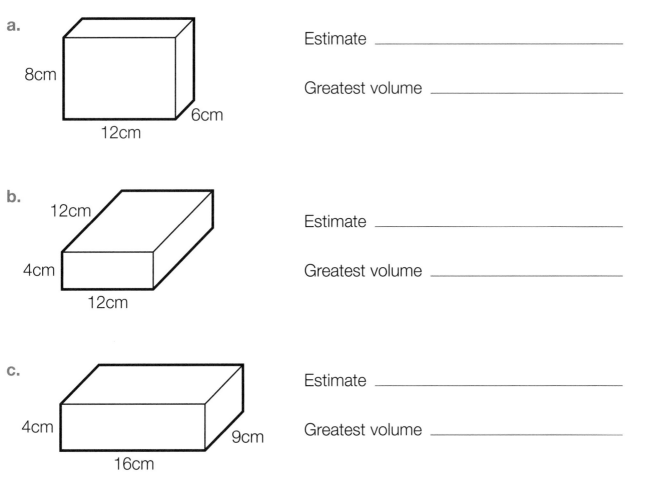

a.

8cm
12cm
6cm

Estimate _____

Greatest volume _____

b.

12cm
4cm
12cm

Estimate _____

Greatest volume _____

c.

4cm
16cm
9cm

Estimate _____

Greatest volume _____

Circles

When drawing circles, you should use a ruler to set the compass to the radius length.

There are important relationships between circle parts to learn, especially between radius and diameter and diameter and circumference.

1. Label the three parts of the circle shown.

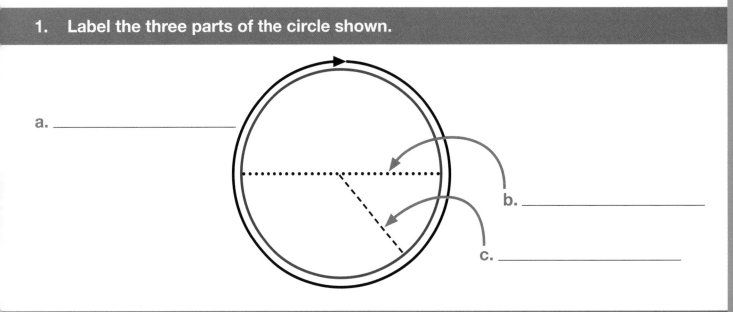

a. _____

b. _____

c. _____

2. Draw circles with the following diameter measurement. The circles can overlap.

a. 4cm

b. 1.5cm

c. 3.5cm

3. Measure the radius and the diameter of each circle. What do you notice about the measurements in each case?

_____

4. **Draw circles with the following radius measurement.**

a. 1cm

b. 2cm

c. 3cm

5. **Measure the diameter of each of these circles with a ruler. Then use a piece of string to measure the circumference as accurately as you can. What do you notice about the two measurements in each case?**

_____

6. **Draw a large circle. Find out what the following circle words mean. Mark them on your circle.**

semicircle * quadrant * arc * chord * segment * sector

Measuring and drawing angles

A right angle is 90°. When you estimate an angle, think about how much bigger or smaller the angle is compared to a right angle. When you measure angles, make sure your protractor is positioned accurately and you are reading off the size of the angle on the correct scale.

1. **Look carefully at each of these angles. Estimate the size of the angle, and then measure it carefully with a protractor.**

a.

Estimate _____

Measurement _____

b.

Estimate _____

Measurement _____

c.

Estimate _____

Measurement _____

d.

Estimate _____

Measurement _____

e.

Estimate _____

Measurement _____

f.

Estimate _____

Measurement _____

2. **Now draw these angles, using a protractor to measure accurately.**

   a. 69° angle   **b.** 101° angle   **c.** 88° angle

In the net

The net of a 3D shape is the flat shape that can be folded and stuck together to make the 3D shape. Take some clean food boxes apart to see what their nets look like. It will help to look at fully-made-up versions of the shapes before attempting to draw out their nets.

1. Kate is having a little trouble drawing the nets of solid shapes. Help her to complete the net for a cube and a triangular prism.

2. Here is the net for a cuboid.
Robert wants to cut it out and stick it together.
Draw the minimum number of flaps required
so that each edge is securely fastened.

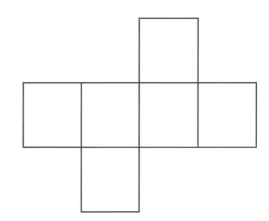

3. In this space, draw the net of a square-based pyramid. Use a set-square to draw the base, which must measure 2cm × 2cm.

Picture coordinates

Coordinates give accurate positions on the grid. They are worked out by reading the horizontal axis first (across) and then the vertical axis (up or down). Make sure coordinates are written in the correct style, for example (−3, 2).

Design a coordinate picture for a friend to try.

1. Use the grid above to plan your design. Your design must go into all four quadrants.

2. Write down the coordinates of your design and give them to your partner to copy onto a blank coordinate grid. Don't let your partner see your picture until they have finished. Were your coordinates accurate? How careful were they in following your instructions?

   Points to remember:

   • The design must be composed of straight lines.

   • The coordinates must be written in order, so that your partner can join them up.

   • You may have more than one set of coordinates, so that it is possible to have smaller shapes inside a larger one (for example, an eye).

Translate and reflect

Sometimes it will be necessary to read and plot coordinates in all four quadrants. Remember, across coordinates must be read first. Make sure the minus signs are shown clearly when you use coordinates that include them.

1. **Draw a suitable regular or irregular shape in the top left-hand quadrant. Label its coordinates.**

2. **Translate the shape once and draw the new shape on the grid. Make a note of the translation, for example 8 right and 3 up, and label the coordinates of the new shape.**

Translation: _____

3. **Reflect the same shape in the vertical and horizontal axes, making sure the coordinates are correct each time. Label the coordinates of each reflection.**

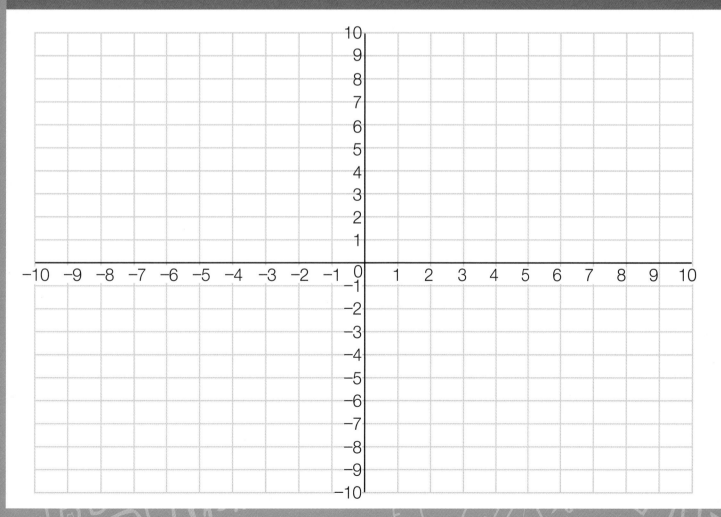

Winning teams' pie chart

Pie charts are divided into sectors. The largest sector shows the item with the highest frequency and the smallest sector show the one with the lowest frequency.

These pie charts show the results of hockey games played by two schools. Southwick School have played 20 matches, while Northport School have played 28 matches.

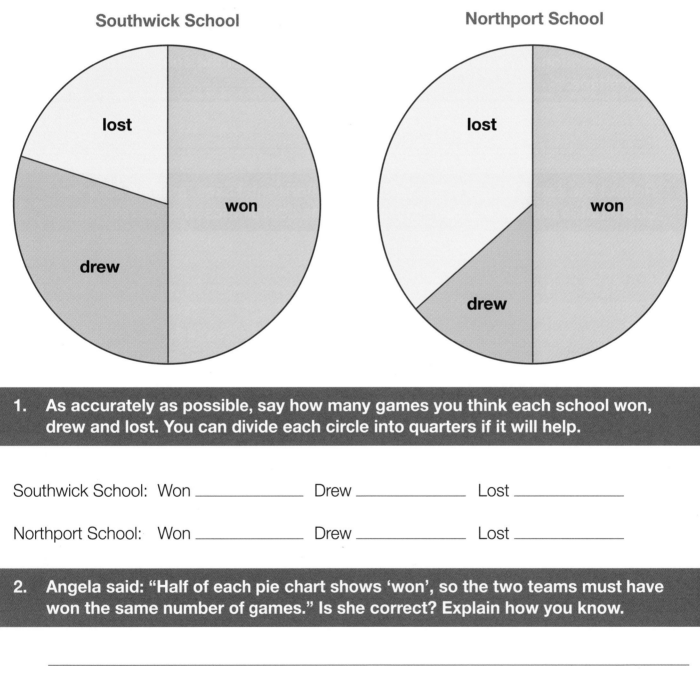

1. **As accurately as possible, say how many games you think each school won, drew and lost. You can divide each circle into quarters if it will help.**

Southwick School: Won _____ Drew _____ Lost _____

Northport School: Won _____ Drew _____ Lost _____

2. **Angela said: "Half of each pie chart shows 'won', so the two teams must have won the same number of games." Is she correct? Explain how you know.**

_____

_____

Interpret a line graph

A line graph is able to show and compare two sets of information. It is useful for comparing two sets of information over a period of time.

This line graph shows the votes cast for the **Red Party** and the **Blue Party** in the last six elections. The points have been joined in each case to show trends over a period of time.

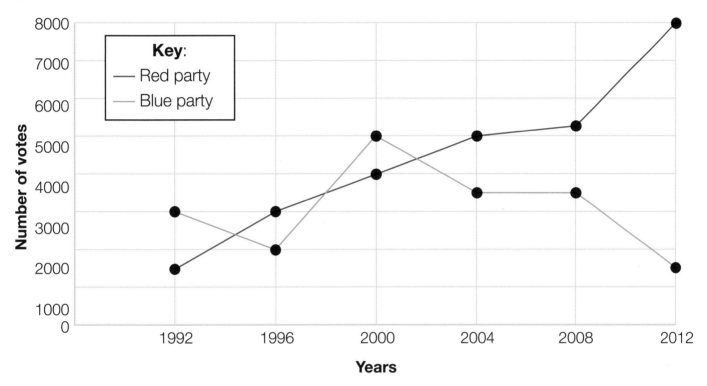

1. Give the highest and lowest vote for both parties. _____

2. How many votes in total did the Red Party get in 2000 and 2004? _____

3. How many votes in total did the Blue Party get in 2008 and 2012? _____

4. In which years did the Blue Party achieve the same number of votes? _____

5. In which years did the Blue Party do better than the Red Party? _____

6. Which party has grown steadily in popularity? _____

7. Describe the performance of the Red Party in the twenty-year period of the elections.

   _____

Progress chart

Making progress? Tick (✔) the cogs as you complete each section of the book.

	Most questions completed	All questions completed
Number and place value	○	○
More practice?		
Calculation	○	○
More practice?		
Fractions, decimals and percentages	○	○
More practice?		
Ratio and proportion	○	○
More practice?		
Algebra	○	○
More practice?		
Measurement	○	○
More practice?		
Geometry: properties of shapes	○	○
More practice?		
Geometry: position and direction	○	○
More practice?		
Statistics	○	○
More practice?		

Answers

The answers are given below. They are referenced by page number and where applicable, question number. The answers usually only include the information the children are expected to give.

Page number	Question number	Answers
6–7	1a	601
	1b	4009
	1c	20,603
	1d	1,620,491
	1e	407,107
	1f	26,300
	1g	300,000
	1h	4900
	1i	2,407,583
	1j	53,724
	1k	80,005
	1l	610
	1m	80,500
	1n	20,630
	1o	4090
	2a	Three thousand and twenty
	2b	Eight thousand, two hundred
	2c	Twenty-seven thousand, five hundred and six
	2d	Seven hundred and eight thousand and ninety
	2e	Four million, seven hundred and eighty thousand, nine hundred and nine
	3a	1275
	3b	40,089
	3c	269,700
	4a	0.3
	4b	0.05
	4c	0.012
	4d	0.8
	4e	0.2
	4f	0.23
	4g	0.2
	4h	0.4
8	1a	£4300
		£36,700
		£843,000
		£900
	1b	1000km
		3000km
		9000km
		484,000km
	1c	50,000 miles
		460,000 miles
		790,000 miles
		850,000 miles
	2a	85cm
	2b	444cm
	2c	790cm
	3a	1000kg
	3b	44,000kg
	3c	102,000kg
	4a	Answers will vary.
	4b	Answers will vary.
	4c	Answers will vary.
	4d	Answers will vary.

Page number	Question number	Answers
9	1a	−2
	1b	−4
	1c	−6
	1d	0, 3, 6
	1e	−2, −6, −10
	1f	6, 4, 2, 0, −1, −3
	1g	−8, −4, −2, 0, 5, 7
	1h	−8, 1, 4
10	1a	500,000
	1b	£2,500,000
	1c	£5,250,000
	1d	£6,500,000
	1e	445,000,000km
	2a	5,500,000
	2b	300,000
	2c	7,250,000
	3a	1,200,000
	3b	6,700,000
	3c	4,450,000
	4a	60,000
	4b	4,000,000
	4c	100
	4d	200,000
	4e	7
	4f	10,000,000
11	1	47°C
	2	−21°C
		39°C
		60°C
	3	82°C
12	1	$2 \times 32 = 64, 4 \times 16, 8 \times 8 = 64$
	2	$1 \times 6.4 = 6.4, 2 \times 3.2 = 6.4, 4 \times 1.6 = 6.4, 8 \times 0.8 = 6.4$
		$0.1 \times 64 = 6.4, 0.2 \times 32 = 6.4, 0.4 \times 16 = 6.4, 0.8 \times 8 = 6.4$
		$64 \div 10 = 6.4, 6.4 \div 2 = 3.2, 6.4 \div 4 = 1.6, 6.4 \div 8 = 0.8,$
		$64 \div 6.4 = 10, 6.4 \div 3.2 = 2, 6.4 \div 1.6 = 4, 6.4 \div 0.8 = 8$
	3	$1 \times 0.64 = 0.64, 2 \times 0.32 = 0.64, 4 \times 0.16 = 0.64, 8 \times 0.08 = 0.64$
		$0.64 \div 1 = 0.64, 0.64 \div 2 = 0.32, 0.64 \div 4 = 0.16, 0.64 \div 8 = 0.08$
13	1	32 = 1, 2, 4, 8, 16, 32
		19 = 1, 19
		72 = 1, 2, 3, 4, 6, 8, 9, 12, 18, 24, 36, 72
		83 = 1, 83
		53 = 1, 53
		37 = 1, 37
		41 = 1, 41
		28 = 1, 2, 4, 7, 14, 28
		67 = 1, 67
		96 = 1, 2, 3, 4, 6, 8, 12, 16, 24, 32, 48, 96
	2	$48 = 3 \times 2^2 \times 2^2$
		$72 = 3^2 \times 2^3$
		$80 = 5 \times 2^2 \times 2^2$
		$56 = 2^3 \times 7$

Page number	Question number	Answers
14–15	1a	13,932
	1b	12,292
	1c	72,286
	1d	199,875
	1e	274,400
	1f	574,209
	1g	219,146
	1h	554,904
16	1	Answers will vary, accept any reasonable estimate.
	2	Look for ideas including finding the amount of bread eaten in a year and then strategies to multiple by 25.
	3	Answers will vary, check long multiplication method used.
	4	Answers will vary.
	5	Answers will vary.
17	1a	1337
	1b	2888
	1c	8716
	1d	6695
	1e	2326km
	1f	5459kg
	1g	£11,142
	1h	7050ml or 7.05l
	2a	£10
	2b	6672
	2c	1,006,110
18–19	1a	47
	1b	75
	1c	194
	1d	126
	1e	234
	1f	112
20–21	1a	24
	1b	34
	1c	58
	1d	65
	1e	$47\frac{8}{16}$ or $\frac{1}{2}$
	1f	$38\frac{8}{24}$ or $\frac{3}{4}$
	1g	$47\frac{6}{18}$ or $\frac{1}{3}$
	1h	$68\frac{10}{15}$ or $\frac{2}{3}$
22		Answers will vary. For example, 894 ÷ 6 = 149
23	1a	102
	1b	76
	1c	216
	1d	125
	1e	219
24	1a	13
	1b	30
	1c	32
	1d	11
	1e	19

Page 25

Amount	5p	16p	23p	Workings
30p	6			6 × 5 = 30
31p	3	1		(3 × 5) + 16 = 31
32p		2		2 × 16 = 32
33p	2		1	(2 × 5) + 23 = 33
34p	-	-	-	
35p	7			7 × 5 = 35
36p	4	1		(4 × 5) + 16 = 36
37p	1	2		(2 × 16) + 5 = 37
38p	3		1	(3 × 5) + 23 = 38
39p		1	1	16 + 23 = 39
40p	8			8 × 5 = 40

Page number	Question number	Answers
26	2a	57 + 29 + 63 = 149 + Emma's cards = Answers will vary.
	2b	Answers will vary. For example, Maths = 60 minutes daily so 60 × 5 = 300 minutes
	2c	Answers will vary e.g. Pens = 5 so 345 ÷ 5 = 69 sheep per pen
	2d	Answers will vary e.g. Swims 1000m at weekend so (5x500) + (2x1000) = 2500 + 2000 = 4500m
27	1a	4 × £500 = £2000
	1b	3 × £510 = £1530
	1c	5 × £320 = £1600
	1d	(2 × £250) + (3 × £320) = £1460
	2a	£1984
	2b	£1527
	2c	£1585
	2d	£1445
28–29	1a	1, 2
	1b	1, 2, 4
	1c	1, 2,
	1d	1, 2, 3, 4, 6, 12
	1e	1, 2, 4
	1f	1, 3, 5, 15
	1g	1, 2
	1h	1, 2, 5, 10
	2a	3
	2b	10
	2c	5
	2d	7
	2e	4
	2f	16
	2g	6
	2h	20
	3a	$\frac{3}{4}$
	3b	$\frac{1}{2}$
	3c	$\frac{1}{3}$
	3d	$\frac{3}{5}$
	3e	$\frac{2}{3}$
	3f	$\frac{3}{5}$
	3g	$\frac{1}{3}$
	3h	$\frac{5}{6}$
	3i	$\frac{1}{3}$
	3j	$\frac{9}{10}$
	3k	$\frac{4}{9}$
	3l	$\frac{19}{20}$
	4a	6
	4b	$1\frac{1}{9}$
	4c	$1\frac{1}{5}$ or $\frac{6}{5}$
	4d	$4\frac{1}{5}$
	4e	$9\frac{1}{2}$ or $\frac{19}{2}$
	4f	$2\frac{3}{5}$ or $\frac{13}{5}$
	4g	$4\frac{1}{3}$ or $\frac{13}{3}$
	4h	$4\frac{1}{4}$ or $\frac{17}{4}$
30	1a	$\frac{8}{10} + \frac{7}{10} = \frac{15}{10} = \frac{3}{2}$
	1b	$\frac{4}{8} - \frac{3}{8} = = \frac{1}{8}$
	1c	$\frac{5}{10} - \frac{3}{10} = \frac{2}{10} = \frac{1}{5}$
	1d	$\frac{8}{10} + \frac{5}{10} = \frac{13}{10}$
	1e	$\frac{7}{12} + \frac{9}{12} = \frac{16}{12}$ or $\frac{4}{3}$
	1f	$\frac{5}{8} - \frac{2}{8} = \frac{3}{8}$
	1g	$\frac{7}{10} - \frac{6}{10} = \frac{1}{10}$
	1h	$\frac{8}{12} + \frac{9}{12} = \frac{17}{12}$
	1i	$\frac{5}{10} + \frac{6}{10} = \frac{11}{10}$
	1j	$\frac{15}{24} + \frac{14}{24} = \frac{29}{24}$
	1k	$\frac{3}{6} - \frac{2}{6} = \frac{1}{6}$
	1l	$\frac{7}{8} - \frac{6}{8} = \frac{1}{8}$
	1m	$\frac{11}{12} - \frac{3}{12} = \frac{8}{12}$ or $\frac{2}{3}$

Page number	Question number	Answers
31	1a	$\frac{1}{6}$
	1b	$\frac{1}{7}$
	1c	$\frac{1}{12}$
	1d	$\frac{1}{10}$
	1e	$\frac{1}{28}$
	1f	$\frac{1}{16}$
	1g	$\frac{5}{81}$
	1h	$\frac{1}{8}$
	1i	$\frac{1}{16}$
	1j	$\frac{1}{18}$
	1k	$\frac{1}{14}$
	1l	$\frac{11}{48}$
32–33	1a	$\frac{2}{10} = \frac{1}{5}$
	1b	$\frac{3}{48} = \frac{1}{16}$
	1c	$\frac{6}{36} = \frac{1}{6}$
	1d	$\frac{20}{80} = \frac{1}{4}$
	1e	$\frac{12}{72} = \frac{1}{6}$
	1f	$\frac{20}{60} = \frac{1}{3}$
	1g	$\frac{9}{30} = \frac{3}{10}$
	1h	$\frac{6}{20} = \frac{3}{10}$
	1i	$\frac{10}{20} = \frac{1}{2}$
	1j	$\frac{15}{10} = \frac{3}{2}$ or $1\frac{1}{2}$
	1k	$\frac{28}{28} = 1$
	1l	$\frac{77}{44} = \frac{7}{4}$ or $1\frac{3}{4}$
	1m	3
	1n	$\frac{24}{6} = 4$
	1o	$\frac{9}{2}$ or $4\frac{1}{2}$
	1p	$\frac{72}{12} = 6$
	1q	$\frac{79}{28} = 2\frac{1}{2}$
	1r	$\frac{63}{24} = 2\frac{5}{8}$
	1s	$\frac{45}{20}$ or $\frac{9}{4}$ or $2\frac{1}{4}$
	1t	$\frac{42}{10}$ or $4\frac{2}{10}$ or $4\frac{1}{5}$
34	1	
	2	
	3	
	4	

Page number	Question number	Answers
35	1a	5 ones or 5
	1b	3 tenths or 0.3
	1c	5 hundredths or 0.05
	1d	3 hundredths or 0.03
	1e	9 thousandths or 0.009
	1f	3 tens or 30
	1g	7 ones or 7
	1h	7 tenths or 0.7
	2	X = 4.2
		Y = 4.7
		Z = 4.9
	3 a–d	Check children's answers.
	4 a–e	Check children's answers.
36	1a	3 eggs 180g of currants 180g of butter 90g of sugar 330g of flour 90ml of milk
	1b	5 eggs 300g of currants 300g of butter 150g of sugar 550g of flour 150ml of milk
	2a	2
	2b	25g
	2c	250g
	2d	120g
	2e	100ml
37	1	40%
	2	35%
	3	25%
	4	182
38		$7c + 3b = 49 + 9 = 58$ $2b = 2 \times 3 = 6$ $(ba)^2 = 12 \times 12 = 144$ $eb = 9 \times 3 = 27$ $2d \times 6 = 10 \times 6 = 60$ $bc = 3 \times 7 = 21$ $4e \div 2b = 36 \div 6 = 6$ $e \div b = 9 \div 3 = 3$ $2d + 6b = 10 + 18 = 28$ $ed = 9 \times 5 = 45$ $a^2 = 4 \times 4 = 16$
39	1a	$9n$
	1b	$12y$
	1c	$lw = a$ or $l \times w = a$
	1d	$6n$
	1e	$n \div 7$
	2a	30
	2b	16
	2c	50
	2d	20
	2e	80
	2f	300
	2g	2
40	1	13
	2a	17
	2b	51
	3a	46
	3b	108
41	1a	43, 52, 62 The amount you add increases by 1 each time, for example: +5, +6, +7
	1b	14, 8, 5 The amount you subtract is halved each time.
	1c	64, 81, 100 The amount you add increases by 2 each time, for example, +11, +13, +15
	1d	8/32, 16/64, 32/128 The numerator and the denominator doubles each time.
	1e	M, S, Z You add 1 more to the number you count on by to get the letter for example, +3 = D, +4 + H, +5 = M
	1f	202, 607, 1822 You × the previous term by 3 and then add 1 to get the next number in the sequence.
	2a	Answers will vary.
	2b	Answers will vary.
	2c	Answers will vary.

Page number	Question number	Answers
42	1a	25, 27, 35, 36; Rule: Amount added to every even nth term increases by 1, amount added to every odd nth term decreases by 1
	1b	15, 24, 26, 32; Rule: +2, +6
	1c	15.5, 18, 20.5, 23; Rule: +2.5
	2a	25/8, 30/8, 37/8, 46/8; Rule: Amount added to the numerator increases by 1 each time for example +2, +3, +4
	2b	0.15, 0.8, 1.45, 2.1, 2.75, 3.4, 4.05, 4.7; Rule: +0.65 each time
	3a	Rectangle
	3b	8
	3c	I thought of each set of shapes as a set of 5 and used this to help work out the answers for example, for 3b 40 ÷ 5 = 8
43	1a	$4f$
	1b	$15 + n$
	1c	$2g - 2$
	1d	$5h$
	1e	$3g + 3h$
	1f	$5x + y$
	2	The mystery number multiplied by six and added to two = $6x + 2$ Two divided by the mystery number = $2 ÷ x$ Three more than the mystery number = $x + 3$ The mystery number added to two then multiplied by six = $6(x+2)$ The mystery number divided by two = $x ÷ 2$ The mystery number divided by fifty = $x ÷ 50$ Fifty divided by the mystery number = $50 ÷ x$ The mystery number multiplied by itself = x^2
44		Answers will vary; check children's measurements.
45		Answers will vary, check children's measurements.
46	1a	1150
	1b	1275
	1c	1850
	1d	2250
	2a	1.75
	2b	2.15
	2c	8.7
	2d	14.6
	3a	1.275
	3b	3.47
	3c	5.5
	3d	12.578
	4a	4,500
	4b	5,900
	4c	12,350
	4d	10,430
47	1	Check children's drawings.
	2a	32
	2b	48
	2c	80
	2d	24
	2e	40
	2f	72
	3a	25
	3b	37 ½
	3c	12 ½
	3d	9 ½
	3e	34 ½
	3f	47
48	1	Check children's chart, for example, 30 × 2 = 64m, 20 × 3 = 46m Biggest perimeter = 60 × 1 = 122m
	2	124m
49	1	Room 1 = 36m² Room 4 = 52m² Room 2 = 42m² Room 5 = 39m² Room 3 = 52m² Room 6 = 52m²

Page number	Question number	Answers
50–51	1a	64cm³
	1b	343cm³
	1c	216cm³
	1d	160cm³
	1e	8750mm³
	1f	15m³
	2	120cm³ 2cm 2cm 13cm
	3	a and b have the same volume = 360cm³ c = 320cm³ d = 280cm³
	4	All have the same volume.
52–53	1a	circumference
	1b	diameter
	1c	radius
	2a	Check children's drawings.
	2b	Check children's drawings.
	2c	Check children's drawings.
	3	The radius is half the diameter.
	4a	Check children's drawings.
	4b	Check children's drawings.
	4c	Check children's drawings.
	5	The circumference is roughly 3× the diameter.
	6	
54	1a	30°
	1b	72°
	1c	94°
	1d	22°
	1e	109°
	1f	127°
	2a–c	Check children's measurements – allow 2° margin of error.
55	1	Check children's drawings.
	2	Check children's drawings.
	3	Check children's drawings.
56		Check children's drawings.
57	1	Answers will vary.
	2	Answers will vary.
	3	Answers will vary.
58	1	Southwick: Won – 10, Drew – 6, Lost – 4 Northport: Won – 14, Drew – 4, Lost - 10
	2	No because Northport played more games so half of their pie chart is worth 14 matches. This means they won more than Southwick whose half is only representing 10 matches.
59	1	Red – Highest : 8000, Lowest: 1500 Blue – Highest: 5000, Lowest: 1500
	2	9000
	3	5000
	4	2004, 2008
	5	1992, 2000
	6	Red party
	7	It has increased year on year.